STRONG MIND STRONG BODY

Being truly healthy means so much more than feeling fit and doing the right amount of exercise. It's also much more than eating a healthy and balanced diet, full of leafy greens and enough fruit and vegetables for the doctor to be happy.

This is because to be truly healthy, your mind also needs to be healthy. You need a strong body and a strong mind, together. One without the other doesn't work.

This journal is packed with fulfilling exercises to stretch and support you mentally and physically, including meditations, yoga practices, breathing techniques, self-reflection, top tips for a balanced diet, and positive eating patterns, as well as space to record and reflect your thoughts along the way.

CONTENTS

KICKSTART YOUR HEALTH DRIVE

STRONG

EMPOWERING ACTIVITIES

HELPFUL HOW-TO TIPS

STRONG

REFLECTIVE JOURNAL PAGES

igloobooks

igloobooks

Published in 2021
First published in the UK by Igloo Books Ltd
An imprint of Igloo Books Ltd
Cottage Farm, NN6 0BJ, UK
Owned by Bonnier Books
Sveavägen 56, Stockholm, Sweden
www.igloobooks.com

1021 001
2 4 6 8 10 9 7 5 3 1
ISBN 978-1-83903-571-5

Written by Philip Harrison

Designed by Simon Parker
Edited by Hannah Cather

Printed and manufactured in China

BALANCED DIET

EMPOWER YOUR MIND

POSITIVE LIFESTYLE

Getting Started

Hello! Let's begin with a few questions about your current patterns with healthy eating and healthy living.

How often do you exercise at the moment?

Do you ever do any visualisation or meditation?

Do you have a balanced diet?

Would you say your mind is as strong as your body? If not, which is stronger?

Now write some initial notes on why you think having both a healthy mind and a healthy body is so important:

Self-Portrait

One of the main requirements for a healthy mind is learning to love yourself. All your faults, your powers, your ups and downs – every single bit. You need to learn to love what you see, hear, and feel about yourself every time you look in the mirror.

Write a compliment to yourself below and give yourself some love!

....

What would you say are your best qualities?

....

What are three things you love about your appearance?

....

List three things you're grateful for about yourself.

....

....

....

In the mirror below, draw a self-portrait and think about what's great about you. Annotate the picture with things you love about yourself. Self-love is crucial for helping you to maintain a strong mind and a strong body.

It's easy to stress about the things that we don't like about ourselves, but rarely do we try to think about what we love about ourselves. It can feel embarrassing or unfamiliar, but reminding yourself about all of the reasons why you are amazing is so important.

Write down some positive words and phrases that describe you:

....

....

....

....

....

Which word in the above list resonates most with you?

....

What makes you such a good friend?

....

Give yourself three bits of praise below:

- ....
- ....
- ....

See! There are so many things to love about you! Whether you like the sound of your name or your choice in books, compile a list of things that you love and appreciate about yourself.

Things I love about me:

....

....

....

....

....

Keep this list safe and read over it when you need a positive reminder of all the good things that you bring to the world.

Affirmations

Positive affirmations are brilliant for boosting your self-belief. Incorporating them into your breathing exercises can help you to focus on actualising your goals. Take a look at these examples of positive affirmations. Which ones in particular speak to you?

Choose a few of them and insert them into your morning routine to help start your day with positivity:

- Take a deep breath in and then out.
- On your next inhale, think of your affirmation.
- On the exhale, continue with "I am open to it all".
- Repeat several times.

A mistake is a memorable lesson if you can learn something from it.

Be the love that you are looking for.

Speak to yourself with love.

Finding your true worth is the richest you will ever be.

Try to change what you can and learn to love what you can't.

Try your best!

Let your mistakes make you, not break you.

There is no perfect, only practice.

Enjoy becoming lost, it's how you'll find most things out.

Hold on to what helps, let go of what doesn't.

You are the speaker and the listener to your own internal voice.

Your best is enough.

"No" is not a negative.

THIS TOO SHALL PASS.

FLAWS INTO FANTASTIC

Recognising your flaws is crucial, because it means accepting you for you, and recognising that you are enough. Flaws are part of being human and no one is perfect. There are so many lessons to be learnt from flaws and mistakes, and having an awareness of this can be very powerful.

Write down three flaws that you think you have and then, by each one's side, write down how that could become a positive. For example: "I worry too much, but worrying means I care and that I want things to be okay".

....

....

....

Flaws and all, you are powerful. Your good bits and your bad bits make up you, and realising that idea is important for self-love, self-acceptance and mental strength.

What are some of your superpowers?

....

What could your superhero name be?

....

Name your best mental power:

....

Name your best physical power:

....

The Magic of Mantras

Mantras are usually a short phrase or sound that you repeat. Reciting them can have similar positive effects to affirmations, but mantras are more bite-size! This might make it a bit more achievable to do every day, or easier and shorter to say as you go about your business.

It is easy to make your own mantras, so that they fit with anything you need to deal with. Start by thinking about a few positive words and short phrases, and feel the positivity and warmth that comes from just imagining them. For example, "self-love", "confidence", "be positive", or "you are the best".

My Mantra List

Now use those positive words and short phrases to make up your own mantras in a list below. They should be easy to remember and repeat.

....

....

....

....

....

....

....

....

....

....

....

....

....

Think of your chosen mantras throughout the day to tap into its feel-good meditative powers. Repeat it as you take a walk, turn on your computer, or as you focus on your breathing. Make it the background beat to everything you do to help invoke a mental clarity and positive state of mind.

Sunshine Breathing

Our emotions can be as unpredictable as the weather, but breathing exercises can help to brighten any darker days.

Find a relaxed position, sitting or lying down, and close your eyes.

Draw your focus to your breathing. Feel each breath go in and each breath leave.

On your next inhale, imagine your breath is a golden wash of sunshine flooding your body with warmth. On your exhale, see any darkness lingering inside you leave with your breath.

Repeat until there is nothing but light inside of you.

Lion's Breath

When you need a boost of self-confidence, give this playful lion's breath exercise a go.

Start by sitting with your legs crossed or folded beneath you, with your bottom resting on your heels. Loop your shoulders up and over towards your back, releasing any tension and creating an open space between the ears and the shoulders. Inhale through the nose and exhale with a hissing "Haaaaah" sound through your mouth. Inhale again and on your next exhale, take your gaze upwards and stick your tongue out and down.

Take five of these lion breaths and be mindful to not hold any tension in your jaw, neck, and shoulders as you repeat. When you've finished, notice how your mind and body feel confident to take the day.

How do you feel after these breathing exercises?

....

....

....

....

....

Cleanse the Airways

Nadi Shodhana is a cleansing yoga breathing practice that can help reduce tension in the mind and bring a calm focus to your day. Find a seated position where you are comfortable and upright, stretching your back nice and tall.

Take a moment to notice your breath. Now, drop your index finger and your middle finger to your palm. Place your thumb over your right nostril and breathe through your left nostril. Gently pause your breath while you move your thumb away. Then, place your ring finger over your left nostril and exhale through your right nostril. Keep your ring finger over your left nostril and inhale. Place your thumb over your right nostril, exhale through your left nostril, and repeat.

In simpler terms, switch nostrils each time you inhale so that you are exhaling through the opposite nostril. Finish this breathing practice by taking a big inhale through both nostrils and release any final tensions with an audible breath out through the mouth.

Belly Breathing

Practising your belly (or abdominal) breathing maximises the positive effects of deep breathing, which can help your relaxation levels and general mental state.

Find a comfortable place to sit or lie down.
Place a hand on your stomach, just below your navel.
Once you are comfy, take a nice long inhale through your nose and feel the air travelling all the way down into your belly.
Feel your hand rise gently as your abdomen expands with the fresh oxygen.
Exhale through your mouth and repeat.
Focus on the slow but powerful rise and fall of your hand.
Try to breathe deeply into the belly every day to keep yourself happy and healthy.

Ujjayi Technique

The "Ujjayi Breath", a yoga breathing technique that is commonly translated as the "victorious breath", is wonderful at giving you a winning attitude to start your day!

Ensure that you're sitting comfortably, then roll your shoulders up and back. Start to deepen your breath, inhaling through the nose and exhaling with a soft audible noise through your mouth – as if you're fogging up a window or mirror with your breath.

Feel a slight tightening in the back of your throat which transforms your breath into the soothing sound of the ocean. When you are comfortable with this, close your mouth and continue the exercise by breathing in through the nose and out through the nose. Try to continue making the soft sound with your mouth now closed.

Stay mindful to the sound of your breath and tap into a more triumphant you.

Inhalation Inspiration

Discover the full potential of your breath by experimenting with this 2:4:2 exercise. The principle is that you inhale for the count of two, exhale for four, pause for two. When it comes to pausing, don't make this an emergency stop. Instead, think of it as approaching the top of a hill before rolling down the other side of it.

Once you've wrapped your head around the 2:4:2 ratio, experiment with different ratios and find what suits you. Maybe inhale for three, exhale for six, pause for three. Then, practise whatever fills you with the greatest sense of positive focus.

How does this exercise make you feel? ....

....

....

....

What is your preferred breathing ratio? Why? ....

....

Archer's Breath

In archery, many instructors will encourage you to take a deep breath before you release your arrow to maximise your chances of hitting your target.

For this exercise, channel your inner archer and, as you inhale, imagine your target is in clear sight. Before you release your arrow of intent, exhale your breath with calm control.

Try doing this breath when you have clear intentions that you need to achieve and want to be filled with a positive focus.

How does this exercise make you feel? ....

....

Which goals do you imagine as your target? ....

....

....

....

....

....

The Power of Yoga

Yoga is a powerful way to exercise the mind and the body at the same time, while also thinking about breathing techniques and mental clarity. It's an all-encompassing form of exercise that will strengthen mind and body, and get both working effectively.

Have you ever done yoga before? One way to get into it is by trying out a few basic poses and seeing how you feel.

Cobra Pose

- Lie on your stomach, with the tops of your feet resting on the floor.
- Place your hands, with palms downwards, to just in front of your chest.
- Slowly raise the upper half of your body, keeping your hips and thighs in contact with the floor.
- Tilt your head back and relax into the pose.

Warrior Pose

- Stand up tall, with your feet wide apart.
- Ground yourself by planting your feet firmly on the floor and parallel to each other.
- Start to turn your body to the right-hand side, turning your right foot as you do so. You should end up with your right foot pointing to the right side, while your left foot is still pointing forwards.
- Slowly raise your arms to shoulder height, so they're parallel to the floor.
- Turn your head to the right and bend your right knee over the ankle.

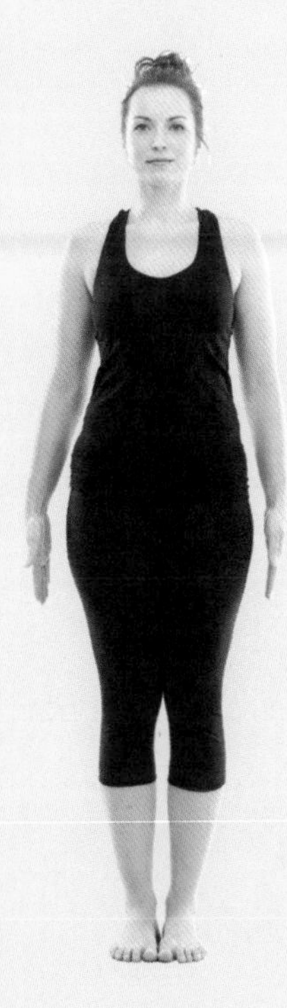

Mountain Pose

- Stand up tall, with your arms down by your side and the palms of your hands facing into your body.
- Ensure that your feet are planted firmly on the floor, together and facing forward.
- Loosen your neck, shoulders, and arms, and relax into the pose.
- Gently straighten your neck, legs, and back, and keep your head up tall.

BOOST YOUR HAPPY

Exercise can have hugely positive effects on your moods, boosting circulation and producing feel-good endorphins. Think about ways in which you can make some small changes to your everyday life to increase your daily activity.

It could be walking to work instead of driving, taking stairs over lifts, or doing your food shop in-store rather than online. Everyone's physical capabilities are unique to them, so always check with your doctor before making any big changes to your routines.

Try making just one active change in your daily life at a time and see how it affects your mood. Use the space on the opposite page to record these little changes and how they made you feel.

Active Changes

How I Feel

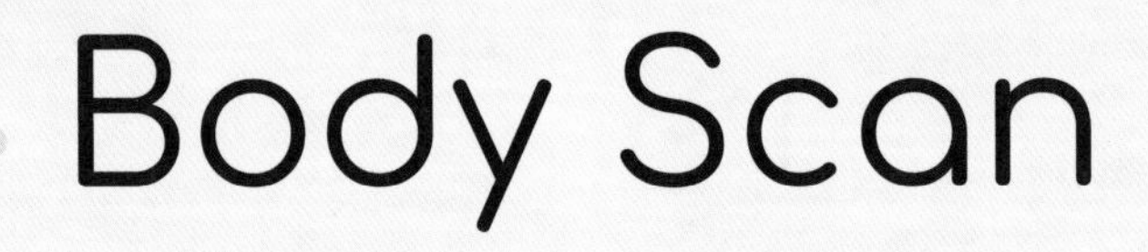

Body Scan

Checking in with your body makes you more aware of your needs and more able to make the positive changes required.

Begin by lying down. Take a moment to get rested. Notice the parts of your body that are making contact with the surface that you are lying on, be it a bed, grass, or carpet.

Take your awareness to your breathing and enjoy a couple of regular breaths or perhaps some belly breaths. Starting at the tips of your toes, begin mentally scanning your body. Notice how every part of you is feeling today.

What are your energy levels like? Are you tired? Is your foot fidgeting? Are you thirsty? Do you have a headache or cold?

Continue the scan through your legs, arms, torso, and face, until you have checked in with your entire body. When you listen to your body, it often tells you what it needs, so try to do a full scan regularly.

- If there are any problem areas, such as a bad knee, or a strained muscle in your arm, take extra time on these. Massage them with a free hand, then squeeze and release them.
- Write down how you feel before and after your scan. These notes will motivate you for next time.
- Be in the right mood and frame of mind before starting, or wait until you are.
- Take time getting comfortable and ready.

Wonderful Wandering

Begin your day by taking an early morning walk. Even if this means setting your alarm fifteen minutes earlier than normal to take a five-minute or ten-minute stroll, the positive benefits of doing so can be felt.

It could mean doing a lap of the garden or getting off a stop or two earlier on your bus journey, but however it's done, a walk boosts energy levels and allows the mind a period of energised focus to start your day right.

Make a plan below for one of your wonderful walks.

My Walking Plan

Time to set my alarm:

....

Where I will walk:

....

A meditation topic for my walk:

....

....

....

....

Write down ways to make each of your walks mindful:

....

....

....

....

....

....

....

....

....

....

Can you think of little things you can do to increase your step count on a daily basis?

....

....

....

....

....

Yoga Poses

Here are some more yoga poses to try. Use the instructions and images to help, and remember to breathe slowly and consciously throughout each one.

Butterfly Pose

- Sit on the floor and bring the bottoms of your feet together.
- Rest your hands against your knees, joining your index fingers and thumbs together.
- Straighten your back, neck, and head so that they are stretched upwards.
- Relax into the pose, seeing if you can slowly lower your knees to the floor.

Tree Pose

- Stand up tall and straight, with your head held high.
- Place the sole of one foot onto the inner thigh, calf, or ankle of the opposite leg, depending on your flexibility and how comfortable it feels.
- Make sure that the other foot remains planted on the floor.
- Place the palms of your hands together in a prayer position and raise them to be in front of your heart – or even above your head if you can balance!

Boat Pose

- Sit on your bottom, with your legs stretched out in front of you.
- Make sure that your back is straight and your neck is stretched tall.
- Breathe in and out, and on the next inhalation, slowly begin to raise your arms in time with your legs. Keep both straight.
- Balance for 20 seconds, or whatever feels comfortable, feeling the power in your core.
- Release on an exhale and move your limbs back down to the floor. Repeat.

How do these poses make you feel?..

....

....

....

Which is your favourite one?..

....

....

....

Did they help you to feel strong mentally and physically?......................................

....

....

....

....

Do you know any more yoga poses?...

....

....

....

....

Mini Exercises

Here are some easy feel-good exercises to get your blood pumping and your pulse racing! The beauty of these exercises is that they can be slotted into your day, so make sure to keep them simple and not stressful. Enjoy!

Squats

Plant both feet firmly on the ground, parallel to each other, then slowly bend your knees, making sure not to lean too far forwards. Squat to where feels comfortable and repeat. Do a few rounds of five squats and feel the burn! You could do this first thing in the morning, while waiting for the toaster to pop, or when you're in a phone queue.

Jog & March

This is a great one for getting your heart pumping! Start by marching on the spot like a soldier and feel yourself getting into a rhythm. Once you have done this for 20 seconds, start jogging lightly on the spot for another 20 seconds. Repeat another time, and again if you feel like it. Remember to bring your knees up during the marching!

Sit-ups or Crunches

Either will do, but both are great exercises for working your core. Lie down on your back on the floor, bending your knees and bringing your feet up so that they rest on the floor. Slowly lift your head and neck off the floor, placing your hands behind your head or ears. Do this during an advert break on the TV or just before bed!

Star Jumps

If you find a spare moment in the day, do a couple of rounds of star jumps to make you feel good and to get all of your body moving. Stretch your arms out wide and keep your jumps low. It's a classic! Star jumps are really good to do first thing in the morning, as they got your blood pumping, ready to face the day.

Which is your favourite of these exercises? Can you think of some more simple, short exercises you could do around your daily life?

Fun Ways to Work Out!

Don't forget that getting active can be fun. It doesn't have to be about super-intense sessions on the cycling machine, or exercises that leave you feeling exhausted. There are lots of ways to make working out enjoyable.

Dancing – Put your favourite music on and bust out some moves, making sure that you keep moving (and grooving) most of the time. Throw your arms in the air and shuffle your feet. Do anything that you like! Freestyle away or pretend you're in a band or a famous dance troupe. Literally dance as though no one is watching. Your heart will be pumping and you'll be full of happy feelings.

Kitchen Aerobics – There is no need for the gym when you can pump some iron in the kitchen! Make weights out of tin cans, mop the floor while doing some lunges, use the kitchen counters as a barre for stretching against and for balance, and get some steps in while the kettle boils. All from the comfort of your own home!

Laughter Workout – There is nothing better than laughing too hard, so why not make it into a fun workout activity? Start chuckling at something, and then make the laugh bigger and bigger, until you are giggling like never before. You will soon notice a feeling in your abs and your core – it should feel like a tightening around the stomach. And the great thing is that you'll hardly notice those muscles working, because you'll be too busy laughing!

Walking & Talking – Perhaps you're due to have a call with someone, or are long overdue a chat with your friend. One way to make this really healthy is to be on the move while you take the call. Don't be lazy and get moving! As you speak, go for a walk around the house, march on the spot, stroll down your road, or around the lounge. It all makes a difference. Your step count could be through the roof!

Can you list more fun ways to exercise?

....

....

....

....

....

....

....

....

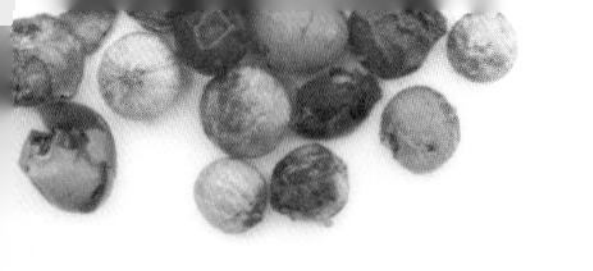

Healthy Eating

Everyone can find a way of eating healthily that suits their lifestyle, income, cooking ability, and taste buds. Healthy eating doesn't have to be difficult and it doesn't mean eating lots of things you don't like. In fact, you're more likely to eat healthily if you enjoy it! All you need to know are a few basic facts about what is healthy, and the starting point for this is a balanced diet.

A balanced diet

A balanced diet means eating the right mixture of food to nourish your body in all the ways that are necessary for health. You don't have to balance it perfectly every day - it's the overall picture that matters.

Here are the main food types you should be eating:

Fruit and vegetables

Fruit and vegetables contain the majority of vitamins that are needed for healthy skin, hair, and general health, including protection for our immune system. They also contain fibre, which helps to keep our digestive system healthy.

Starchy carbohydrates

(rice, pasta, potatoes, bread)

Carbohydrates - or carbs, as they're often called - give us energy. They are an essential part of a balanced diet, and they're very important if you are doing a lot of exercise or have a busy lifestyle.

Dairy and alternatives

Dairy products are vital for your bones and teeth. They may have a positive impact on your mental health, too. Some people are allergic to milk and milk products, or may choose to avoid them for other reasons, but healthy alternatives, such as almond milk and coconut milk, are readily available.

Protein

(beans, pulses, fish, eggs)

Protein keeps our muscles healthy and strong, and allows us to grow and repair cells. Some high-protein foods also contain chemicals such as fatty acids, which play a vital role in protecting our metabolism and hormones.

How much food do I need?

Adult women need around 2,000 calories per day and men need around 2,500 (the number of calories a type of food has refers to the amount of energy contained in it). If you are counting calories, you should include all of your food and drinks. If you take part in a lot of sport or have a very physical job, your body will be using more energy and so may require more calories to fuel itself.

Some medical conditions require a higher or lower calorific intake - always follow the advice of your doctor.

Journal moment

List three small changes you could make to improve the balance of your diet. For example, having a banana instead of a couple of biscuits.

1...

2...

3...

Food Groups

Carbohydrates

The starchy foods that we eat every day (bread, pasta, rice, potatoes, cereal) provide us with a range of important nutrition, including energy, fibre, B vitamins, including folate or folic acid, calcium, and iron.

- You should eat roughly the same amount of starchy food as fruit and vegetables.
- There are some diets that recommend cutting out carbs altogether. It's important to remember that carbs are an essential part of your diet and should be included in the long term.
- Wholegrain bread, brown pasta, and rice, and potatoes with the skin left on, are all good sources of fibre, and have more healthy vitamins and minerals than their refined equivalents.. Potato skins are also a great source of vitamin C.

Fruit and vegetables

Variety is key with fruit and vegetables. Trying to include ones of different colours – "eating a rainbow" – will mean you get all of the vitamins your body needs to thrive. For example, a banana is rich in potassium and fibre as well as carbohydrates, whereas oranges are rich in vitamin C and antioxidants.

- One portion is around 80g (roughly the size of your fist) and most guidance suggests eating at least five portions a day. Frozen and tinned fruits and vegetables also count.
- Try to eat more vegetables than fruit, as they are lower in sugar and kinder to your teeth.
- All of your five portions should be of different things.
- A heaped tablespoon of dried fruit counts as a portion.
- Only one portion of your five a day should come from fruit juice. The sugar in juice can be bad for your teeth, and as it doesn't contain much fibre, drinking a lot of juice can lead to sugar spikes that cause health issues in the long term.

Protein

With so many people now following vegetarian and vegan diets, and with lots of people reducing their meat intake, we are having to rethink the way we incorporate protein into our diets.

- Getting protein used to be difficult for vegetarians, but not any more! As well as eggs, nuts, seeds, lentils, and beans, there are loads of plant-based alternatives in the supermarkets. Make sure that your options include protein and aren't just vegetables in breadcrumbs!
- Eggs are amazing. They not only contain protein, but iron as well.
- Some fish, like tuna and salmon, have oils that are good for brain health.
- Limiting red meat to one or two portions a week can cut your risk of lots of health conditions, including diabetes and heart disease.

Fats and oils

Some fat is essential to our well-being. As well as being good for our skin and mental health, it carries fat-soluble vitamins such as vitamins A, D, E, and K around the body. Fats and oils that are polyunsaturated, such as the ones usually found in plant-based foods, are broadly better for you than saturated fats, which generally come from animal products (although there are exceptions).

- If you're using olive oil on salads, try extra virgin. It is associated with good heart health.
- Whatever fats and oils you choose, remember not to have too much.

Dairy or dairy alternatives

Whether you eat dairy from cows, or dairy alternatives, it's vital to get calcium that comes from dairy products. Dairy can also be a source of protein.

- Dairy products are a good source of fat-soluble vitamins A and D, which are great for your immune system and mood. However, be aware of how much fat you have in your diet overall – too much can be bad for you.
- You may wish to choose low-fat options where available, such as skimmed milk or reduced-fat yoghurt.

Get Cooking!

Cooking and preparing your own food, rather than buying ready meals and takeaways, is a good way to be sure your food is healthy. It can also save you money! Don't think that every meal you prepare has to be a gourmet treat. Most healthy food is simple, easy, and routine.

My cooking journal

Write down a meal you recently cooked from scratch using fresh ingredients.

....

....

....

When did you cook it?..

Who was it for?...

Did you enjoy cooking it?..

What stops you from cooking more?
Time? Expense? Confidence? Lack of ideas?

....

....

....

....

Ideas for simple, cost-effective cooking:

- Two words: jacket potatoes. Vary the filling from beans, tuna, cottage cheese, or egg mayonnaise, and serve with a salad. It's cost-effective and packs a punch with your daily nutrients.
- Soup is 'soup-er' easy! First, invest in a stick blender and keep some low-salt stock cubes or powder in your cupboard. Put vegetables like potatoes, carrots, leeks, parsnips, and onions in a pan, add stock powder and water to cover. Simmer until cooked, then mix with your blender. Make enough for 3 or 4 portions in one go and freeze, if necessary.
- Don't fear the freezer. Lots of vegetables like peas, spinach, and sweetcorn are cheaper to buy frozen.
- Pulses like chickpeas and lentils can be bought tinned or dry, but dry pulses may need to be soaked before use. If you're not good at planning ahead, buy tinned.
- Wrap it up. Wraps are cheap and portable. Fill a wrap with chicken and salad or with houmous, salad, and falafel.
- Break your breakfast toast habit. Instead, try a low-sugar oat cereal with an extra handful of raisins or pumpkin seeds. Bananas, apples, grapes, and mango are all delicious served with yoghurt first thing in the morning, too.
- Porridge - buy a bag of dry oats and add water or milk to cook. You can add sugar, fruit, or syrup to taste.
- Sow the seeds of healthy eating. Pumpkin seeds, sunflower seeds, sesame seeds, and chia seeds can be bought separately and then mixed together in a pot for a lunchbox or daytime snack, or added to salads and cereal.

What will you cook from scratch this week?

Monday: .... Tuesday: ....

Wednesday: .... Thursday: ....

Friday: .... Saturday: ....

Sunday: ....

SHOPPING & STORAGE TIPS

SHOPS

A great place to go for fruit and vegetables is the greengrocers, as they will know a lot about the products they are selling. However, if you don't have a greengrocer nearby, most large supermarkets stock a range of food that is fresh, including organic food.

It isn't necessary to buy the latest 'superfood'. Normal food contains everything necessary for health. Large supermarkets also stock a wide range of dairy-free and gluten-free products, as well as vegetarian foods.

Farmers' markets are a good source of very fresh vegetables, meat, eggs, and cheese (and sometimes home-made bread, too), so give these a try if you can.

A really effective way of buying dry goods (like pasta, rice, lentils, beans, raisins, flour) is to use a plastic-free refill service. These can either be found in shops, or occasionally as a delivery service. These foods are healthy, reduce the use of plastic, and are kind to the planet.

Don't be afraid of tinned or frozen food. Tinned fish, fruit, and vegetables can all be healthy, so long as they are not preserved in too much salt (brine) or syrup (buy peaches or pears in juice). Frozen food is often just as nutritious as fresh food and is much cheaper to buy.

STORAGE

When storing food, soft fruits like strawberries, raspberries, and blueberries might be best kept in the fridge so that they last longer, whereas apples and oranges are fine in your fruit bowl.

Salad is happiest in the fridge, so that it stays crisp and juicy for longer.

Root vegetables and potatoes don't need to be kept in the fridge, so long as they are somewhere that's dark and not too warm.

Always check the use-by date on your meat and dairy products, and store them carefully.

Fresh herbs can be kept in the fridge, or if you have too many to use in one go, freeze them in a bag and then chop them straight from the freezer.
It's also really easy to grow your own herbs if you have a garden or window box.

Fresh herbs are great for cooking healthily, as they flavour your food without the need for salt.

IS IT SAFE TO FORAGE?

Our love affair with convenience means that a lot of food goes to waste. Look out for raspberries and blackberries that are growing wild, or even mulberries, chestnuts, and wild garlic. Never eat anything unless you're sure of what it is, avoid busy roadsides, and steer clear of mushrooms unless you are with an expert!

My Food Heaven!

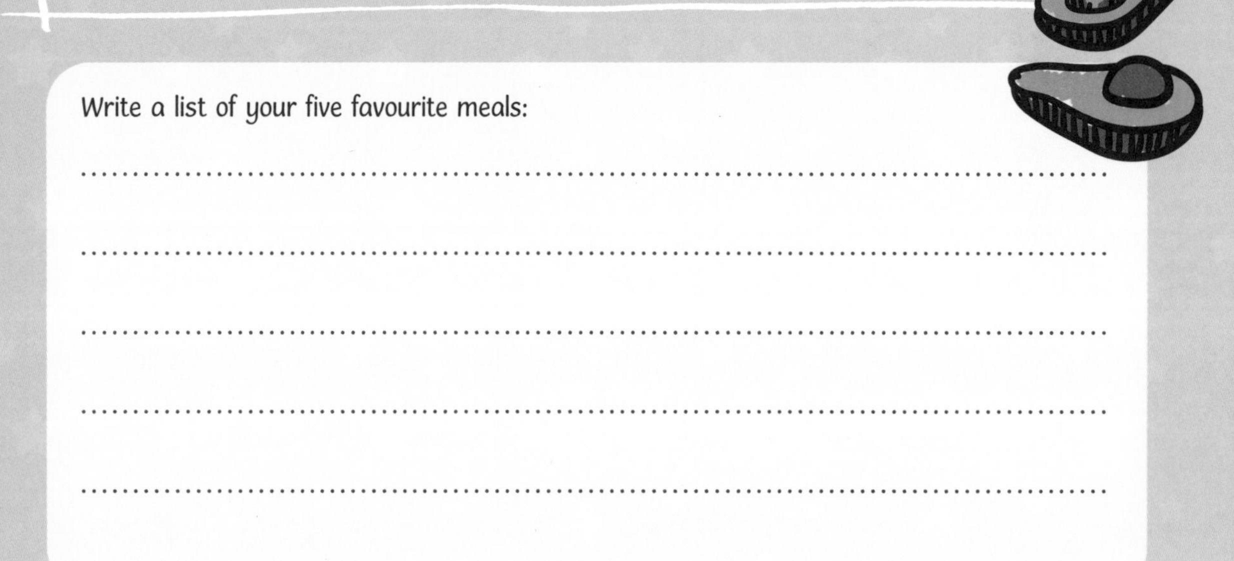

Write a list of your five favourite meals:

....

....

....

....

....

Now, write down any changes that could make each meal healthier. E.g. change fried chicken for grilled chicken, and double cream for yoghurt. Add more vegetables to a home-cooked curry and replace a ready-made stir-fry sauce with fresh spices.

Meal 1

Date: ....

Title: ....

Healthy Changes:

....

....

....

....

....

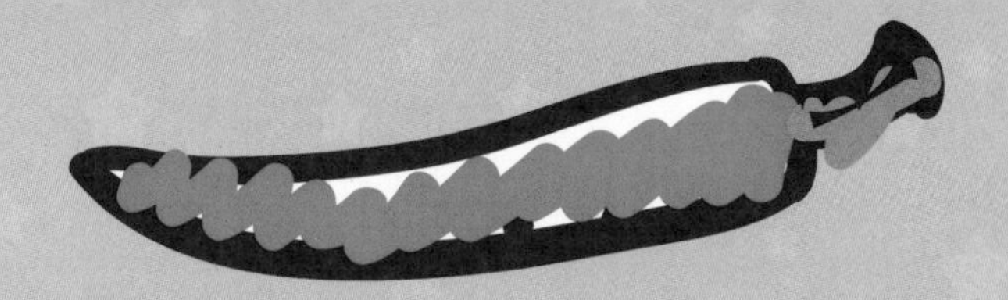

Meal 2

Date: ....

Title: ....

Healthy Changes:

....

....

....

....

....

Meal 3

Date: ....

Title: ....

Healthy Changes:

....

....

....

....

....

Meal 4

Date: ....

Title: ....

Healthy Changes:

....

....

....

....

....

Meal 5

Date: ....

Title:..

Healthy Changes:

....

....

....

....

....

REDUCE YOUR SUGAR... LIFE IS SWEET ENOUGH!

Sugar is a natural source of energy and is present in lots of foods, such as fruit. Too much sugar, particularly if it's refined or 'free' sugar, can cause problems with your health, ranging from tooth decay to diabetes.

NATURAL OR FREE?

Free sugar, the type of sugar that is not good for you, is the kind found in sweets, cakes, chocolate, and in granular form. It's also found in honey and syrups, like maple and golden syrup. Part of the reason it is not good for you is that it has almost no nutritional value other than energy. It gets burned up by the body quite quickly and then makes you feel hungry and tired - a sugar crash.

HOW MUCH IS TOO MUCH?

Nutritionists recommend no more than seven teaspoons of added 'free' sugar per day for adults, and five to six for children. This equates, roughly, to one small chocolate bar.

Most people eat too much sugar without even knowing it. The most difficult added sugar to spot and cut out can be the sugar that's added to sauces and ready meals - things that may not even taste sweet! Tomato sauce and baked beans are two well-known examples of this.

Tips for reducing sugar in your diet:

- Avoid ready meals, sauces, pasta sauces, and takeaways as much as possible. Try to cook fresh when you can, as this will give you a better chance of avoiding hidden sugar.

- Breakfast cereals and granola can contain a lot of sugar. Check what sugar is in whatever you are buying and control your portions. Unsweetened porridge oats can be cooked with milk or water, then mixed with mashed banana, raisins, or a small amount of honey to sweeten. Try some different types of muesli, as this often has less sugar than other cereals.

- Do not buy sweet, fizzy drinks to consume at home and limit fruit juice. If buying squash, look for the 'no added sugar' variety.

- Try not to use too much refined sugar in baking. There are great recipes for flapjacks and oat bars that use bananas instead of sugar.

- Consider trying low-sugar desserts, like fruit salad with unsweetened yoghurt.

- To fight your sugar cravings, keep snacks handy that you enjoy but do not contain sugar.

Time for a Drink

How much water do I need?

The actual amount of fluid you need varies according to age, activity, and circumstances, but a good guide is eight glasses of water – or equivalent – per day. Everyone needs more fluid when it is hot and also when they exercise.

Too little fluid in the body can lead to short-term health problems, like poorer physical and mental performance, and long-term problems like digestion disorders.

Although water is very good for you, a lot of drinks are water-based and therefore also good for hydration.

Good drinks and not-so-good drinks

- Be careful to limit your consumption of juices and smoothies, as these can contain high volumes of sugar and don't always have the fibre content of whole fruit.

- It's best to limit consumption of tea and coffee as these contain caffeine, although tea, especially green tea, is rich in antioxidants.

- Avoid sweet, sugary drinks unless they are a special treat.

- It is possible to drink too much water. The best guide to how much you should drink is what your body tells you – if you feel thirsty, take a drink. Children may need help recognising when they are thirsty. Our sense of thirst decreases as we age, too, so older adults may need to pay more attention to make sure they're drinking enough.

Vitamins & Minerals

There are several vitamins and minerals necessary for good health, which are vitamins A, B (including folic acid), C, D, E, and K, calcium, iron, iodine, zinc, and beta carotene.

There are some other minerals that we need in small quantities.

It sounds like a lot, but most of these are present in your food, so the more balanced and nutritious your diet, the less likely you are to need supplements.

There are two supplements that doctors do sometimes recommend for otherwise healthy people, which are:

Vitamin D

This comes from sunlight, but low levels of sunlight (for example, in winter) may mean that we don't receive enough Vitamin D naturally. Ten micrograms as a supplement is sometimes recommended.

Folic acid

This is necessary for pregnant women as it supports the health of the baby in the womb.

There are other supplements that may help with specific health conditions - take advice from your doctor or registered health professional.

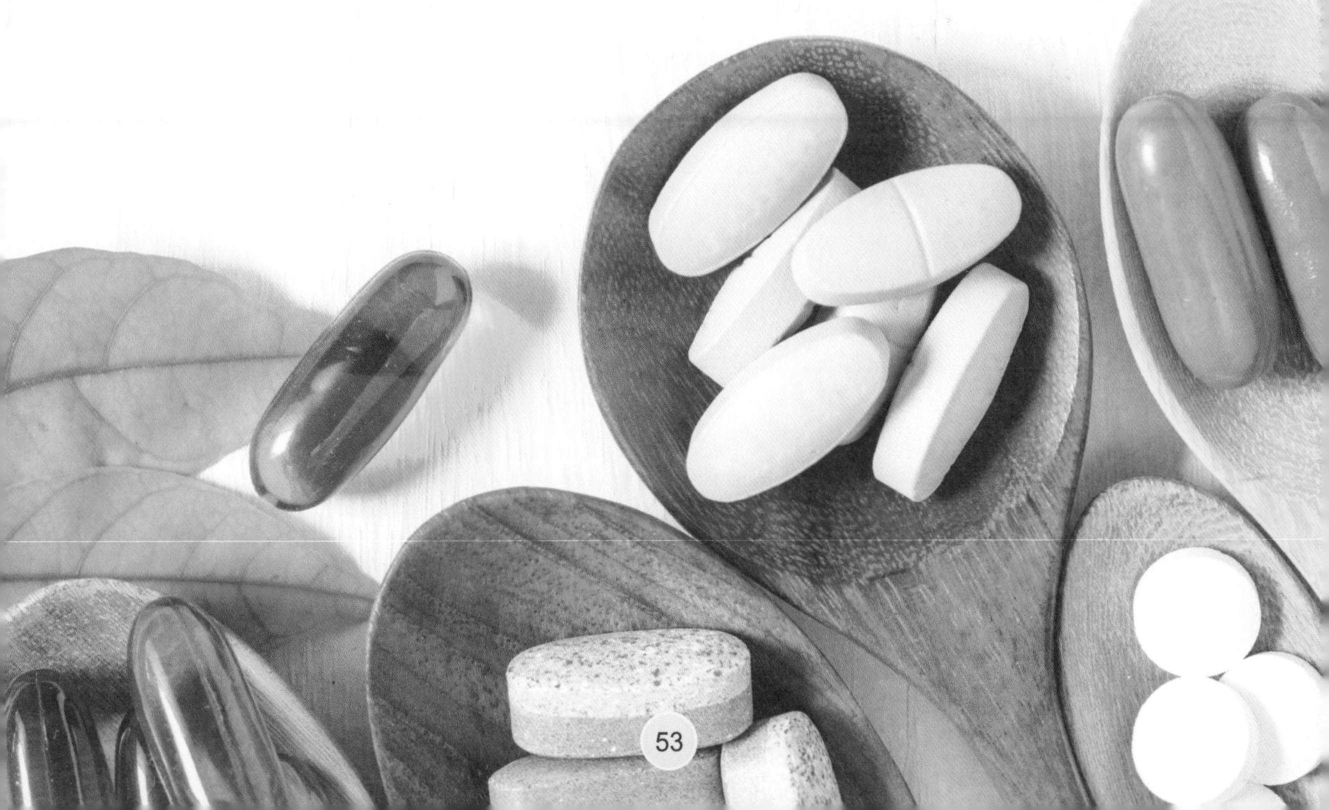

My Eating Pattern

Thinking about your general eating pattern is highly useful, as it'll show what you're having too much of, too little of, and not enough of etc. It's also good to plan meals because you can think about the exact foods you need and therefore avoid any wastage.

Use the questions and prompts below to work out your current eating pattern.

What are your all-time favourite foods?

....

....

Do you eat many fruits and vegetables?..

Do you think that you have a balanced diet?..

What could be done to improve your current eating pattern?.........................

....

What's your top tip for a healthy lifestyle?...

....

On a scale of 1-10, how healthy would you say you are?.................................

What are some of your favourite treats?..

....

....

Have a go at writing out some meal plans, with the goal being to create a balanced diet full of things you enjoy and things that your body is going to thank you for!

Today's Meal Plan:

Breakfast: ....

Lunch: ....

Dinner: ....

Snacks: ....

Treats: ....

Drinks: ....

Have I achieved a balanced diet today?

....

Today's Meal Plan:

Breakfast: ....

Lunch: ....

Dinner: ....

Snacks: ....

Treats: ....

Drinks: ....

Have I achieved a balanced diet today?

....

Today's Meal Plan:

Breakfast: ....

Lunch: ....

Dinner: ....

Snacks: ....

Treats: ....

Drinks: ....

Have I achieved a balanced diet today?

....

Today's Meal Plan:

Breakfast: ....

Lunch: ....

Dinner: ....

Snacks: ....

Treats: ....

Drinks: ....

Have I achieved a balanced diet today?

....

A Plant-Based Diet

There are health reasons and ethical reasons for eating a more plant-based diet. Many people are now choosing to cut out or reduce the amount of meat and dairy in their daily diet.

Meat: the facts

Meat and animal products contain protein, vitamins, and minerals, and can be eaten as part of a balanced diet. However, there are some downsides, particularly if you eat large amounts:

- Red meat and processed meat is associated with higher cholesterol and with some kinds of cancer, such as bowel cancer.
- Red meat is high in saturated fat.
- Processed meat has added salt and other additives.
- Some meat is produced in ways that may reduce the nutritional content and involve animal cruelty.
- There are conservation and animal welfare concerns around the production of animal-based products.

As a result of the concerns around animal-based products, many people have adopted a range of diets with less meat. With each of these, care is needed to make sure that all of the right protein, iron, and other minerals are still part of a person's daily nutrition. Some of these diets are explained below:

- Vegetarian: When people eat no meat or fish, but continue to eat eggs and dairy.
- Vegan: No meat, fish, eggs, or dairy. Many vegans avoid all animal products including leather.
- Pescatarian: No meat, but continues to eat fish and dairy.
- Reduce-atarian: An intention to eat less meat overall.

Give plants a try!

You don't have to give meat or dairy up entirely, but a few swaps might be good for your health. E.g. Try a 'meat-free Monday'.

My 'meat-free Monday' meal ideas:

....

....

....

If you decide to cut down on meat and/or dairy, there is no reason to miss out so long as you follow a few simple steps.

Here are some good plant-based sources of protein, iron, calcium, and vitamin B12, which are nutrients mainly found in meat and dairy. A good mix of these will also provide amino acids, which are necessary for building and repairing cells.

Protein	Iron	Calcium	B12
lentils	pulses	green, leafy veg (e.g. kale, spinach)	yeast extract
pulses	red kidney beans	soya drinks	fortified soya products
beans	chickpeas	anything made with fortified flour, e.g. bread.	fortified breakfast cereals
nuts	dried fruit (e.g. sultanas, figs)	tofu	
seeds	dark green veg (e.g. broccoli, kale, spinach, spring greens)	sesame seeds	
tempeh	wholemeal bread		
tofu	cereals fortified with iron		
textured vegetable protein			

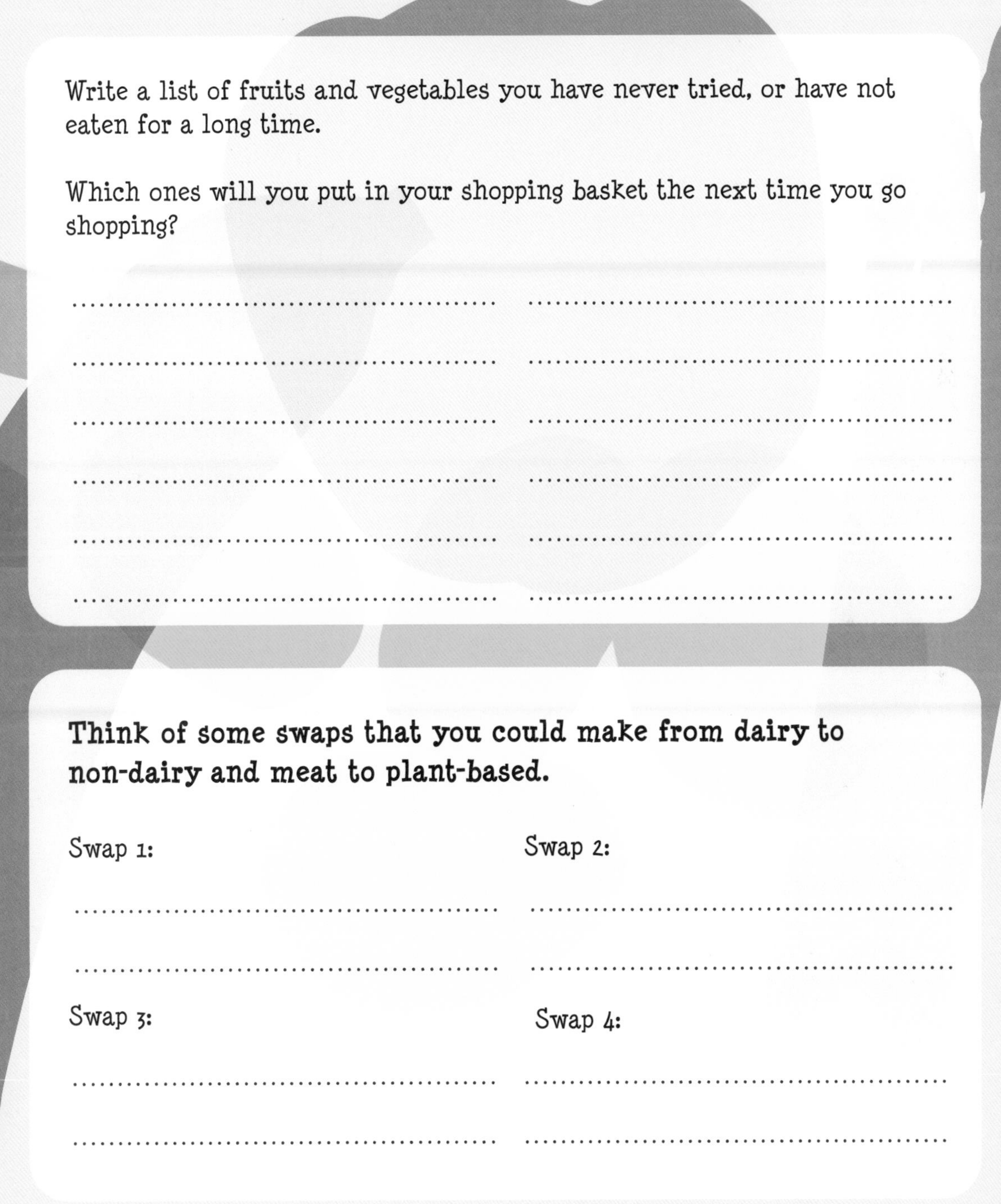

Write a list of fruits and vegetables you have never tried, or have not eaten for a long time.

Which ones will you put in your shopping basket the next time you go shopping?

....

....

....

....

....

....

Think of some swaps that you could make from dairy to non-dairy and meat to plant-based.

Swap 1:

....

....

Swap 2:

....

....

Swap 3:

....

....

Swap 4:

....

....

60-Second Meditation

Set a timer on your phone for a minute and use this time to write down as many positive words, phrases, or sketches as you can in the space below. Don't think too hard about it and see what comes out of your mind.

A positive mind is so helpful for creating a strong mind, so the more you can fill up this page, the better!

Now use some of those words to fill in the little notelets on this page. Create compliments, affirmations and praise for yourself, as well as little notes you'd pass onto someone else. Try and get at least two of the positive words or phrases from the previous page into these messages!

Manifestations

Making Your Dreams into a Reality

Don't be afraid of vocalising what you want and chasing your dreams. Allow yourself to imagine reaching your goals and visualise how it will feel when you do.

Hold onto this feeling as you go about your daily life but also tap into it in private moments to intensify your positive drive.

Write down one of your dreams below:

....

....

....

Now, write down steps for making that dream a reality. Each step should aim to make the dream more concrete and achievable.

....

....

....

....

....

....

....

....

....

What time frame do you envisage for making this dream a reality? Putting a rough deadline on it can help.

....

....

....

Turn Your Potholes into Positives

Failure is part of everyone's life. Things don't always work out how we think they should do,
so we stamp them with a big "FAILED" sign.

Look back on a time in your life that felt as though your endeavours had fallen short. Can you write one of them below?

....

....

....

Now, write down one thing you learnt from that experience. Think about how you are a more experienced and compassionate person from having learnt this.

....

....

....

See if you can fill in the boxes below with more failures that have turned into success stories.

My "Failures"	What I Learnt

Post Box Visualisation

Take a moment to steady your breath and close your eyes. This will help to promote a calm focus. Now visualise yourself in front of a post box, holding an envelope.

As soon as an unhelpful thought or bad memory rears its ugly head, shrink the thought or person down to the size of your envelope. Place the shrunken problem inside the envelope and post it through the post box in front of you.

Do this with each stress or concern that enters your mind; simply shrink, seal, and post it. You may find the same stress popping up, but keep shrinking it to the size of the envelope and it will soon become more manageable.

How do you feel after trying this visualisation?

....

....

....

....

....

....

....

On a scale of 1-10, how stress-free do you feel?

1 2 3 4 5 6 7 8 9 10

Paint Visualisation

To practise both appreciation and patience, try this arty visualisation exercise. Imagine yourself as a blank canvas. Then, begin painting the canvas with things that make you who you are. Try to capture both good and bad memories, like your first break-up and passing your driving test. See it all as brush strokes, colour, texture, and beauty. Now sit in front of your painting and allow it to dry. Notice how some areas are drying faster than others.

As you wait for your creation to dry, focus on your breathing while you appreciate the artwork you have created.

How do you feel after doing this visualisation?

....

....

On a scale of 1-10, how relaxed do you feel now? ....

Don't Mind Your Mood

Emotions are often interlinked with people's moods, but is it possible to feel stressed-out and for there to be a good reason for it? Is anger ever a productive feeling?

Start by trying to recognise the idea that any emotions you feel are totally normal, natural, and vital for your health and well-being. Tell yourself, "I feel this way for a reason", then work out what that reason is.

Things to remember about feelings:

- All emotions are normal and valid.
- Most emotions don't last forever and are simply a reaction to a current situation or thought.
- You should be the controller of your emotions.
- There is a reason for every emotion.

Complete the sentences below and try to think of some positive reasons for your negative emotions.

I sometimes feel angry because...

....

I sometimes feel sad because...

....

I sometimes feel nervous because...

....

I sometimes feel impatient because...

....

Can you think of two examples where your "negative" emotions have turned out to be useful to you? Write about them in the bubbles below.

Dealing with Fears & Anxiety

Fears and anxiety can hamper the ability to have a strong mind and a strong body. The thing to remember is that it's not about trying to flatten down anxious feelings or fears, but accepting them and using them as a springboard for achieving and succeeding.

On a scale of 1-10, how anxious do you feel most of the time? Why?

....

How does anxiety make you feel?

....

....

....

What are some of your fears?

....

....

....

Write down three affirmations that might help you with fear and anxiety:

....

....

....

Give Your Fears & Anxiety the "What If..." treatment!

Every time fear or anxiety starts to creep in, give these feelings the "What if..." treatment. This is a great exercise for encouraging positive thinking and finding an empowering solution to combating negative emotions.

I'm not working fast enough **OR** What if I gave myself more time?

I'm not as good as that person **OR** What if I stopped comparing myself to others?

I'm going to fail **OR** What if I succeed?

What if they say no? **OR** What if they say yes?!

Think of some more examples below...

....

....

....

....

....

....

....

....

Expand the Mind

Travel expands the mind, so why not have a go at thinking up some incredible travel plans and dream destinations? Doing it in your mind makes the travel limitless and without boundaries. What distance will your imagination reach? Feel your mind grow and stretch as you answer the following prompts.

Name your top four bucket-list destinations:

....

....

....

....

If you could go to different countries for breakfast, lunch, and dinner, where would you go?

....

Name a dream city break:

....

What are some amazing activities you would do while travelling?

....

Which language would you most like to learn? ....

Flight Mode Meditation

This meditation is all about zoning out of the daily grind and honing in on your inner thoughts. It's taking some time out for your mind to travel and not allowing any distractions to interfere with your journey.

- Make sure you are sitting or lying comfortably.
- Close your eyes and get used to this new sensation, feeling the light flickering behind your eyelids.
- Check your breathing. Take slow, deep breaths in and out, in and out. Find your rhythm and a pattern.
- Imagine that the tip of your nose is a button that switches your flight mode on and off. What kind of a button is it?
- Now reach up to the button with one of your fingers and press it. You've just switched on your inner flight mode!
- Try to ignore outside distractions, and forget about your phone and the daily jobs. The only things you need to think about are clearing your mind, breathing, and feeling content. Flight mode is a good place to be!

Use flight mode in real life, too!

For a lot of people, their phones can be a constant source of pressure, forever beeping, flashing, and demanding attention. Whether you think your phone is the root of your anxieties or not, try switching it to flight mode for an hour when you can. If you're feeling brave, stretch it to two hours or more, if possible. Do this regularly and you should feel your anxieties reduce.

Social Spring-Clean

This one is for the technoholics! Do you feel like you spend a lot of time on your phone or your laptop, or any other device? Are you having far too much screen time?

Which social media do you use?

....

How much screen time do you have per day?

....

Do you think you have too much screen time?

....

How does going on social media make you feel?

....

....

....

Top Tip!

If there are accounts that make you feel bad in any way, unfollow or silence their notifications so they no longer come up on your feed. Only follow accounts that inspire positivity in you, and see if there are other similar accounts that you could follow for feel-good content!

This page is for thinking about all of the amazing things you can do away from the screen. Fill in the bubbles below with lots of fun activities that will take your eyes away from your device. For example: playing sports, going for a walk, painting, and reading.

Sleep More, Stress Less

A lack of sleep can increase your stress levels. Are you getting less than the recommended 7-9 hours? Even if you are within this guidance, try going to bed one hour earlier than usual.

Ditch the phone and any other screens, and replace them with a book or a journal. Getting into the habit of reading or writing before bed can help promote a more restful sleep and have you walking up a calmer, fresher you!

What's your usual bedtime?

....

What's your bedtime routine?

....

....

....

....

Do you have screen time just before sleeping?

....

If so, what could you swap this with?

....

....

....

....

RESTORING BALANCE

Take a look at the balancing scales on the opposite page. On one side, write a list of all the things you would like to do more of in your life. On the other side, write down all the things you would like to do less of. These might be activities, skills, or habits.

Once you have finished, assess the scales. Is the balance right for you? If not, how can you work to adjust it? What should you be more or less of?

As our lives change, this list will naturally alter, so make sure you come back to this exercise regularly to check that you are achieving the best balance for yourself.

What do you think of your current life/work balance?

....

....

....

....

....

....

....

I should do more of...

I should do less of...

Attitude of Gratitude

There's nothing quite as effective at lifting yourself out of a dark place as listing all the wonderful things in your life that you are grateful for. Whether they are big or small things, people or places, write down a list of things below that help bring a smile to your face.

What I'm grateful for:

....

....

....

....

....

....

Why not extend this list even further? You could find a notebook and use it to continue your gratitude list. Maybe try to write down three things a day, or just when the ideas come to you. Your list will soon grow and you'll recognise that counting your blessings is such a worthwhile thing to do.

The Mindful (Non-Alcoholic) Drinking Game!

Try this game if you are struggling to remember to dedicate time in your life to finding the positive.

Each time you have a drink, be that tea, water, or juice, imagine you are making a toast of thanks to someone or something in your life. The toast can be a short and sweet, like "Thanks for my dogs!" or "Thanks for my family!" or "Thanks for giving me the strength to achieve my goals today!" It could be something longer if you prefer.

Note down some of your toasts below, to help you remember all of the things you are thankful for.

My toasts:

....

....

....

....

....

....

....

Feel-Good in Five!

Fill in the five feel-good blanks below for a quick boost of positivity.

I love .... about myself.

I love the way I ....

I am happy with ....

I love my ....

.... makes me happy.

Add some more feel-good sentences about you below:

....

....

....

....

....

....

Hopefully you should be in a positive head space now, so it's time to focus on your body. The mind and the body work closely together to form a strong person. The exercises listed below are simple ones to do at home or on-the-go, helping you to add a bit of energy to your day.

Here are five little exercises to get your body energised:

While the kettle is boiling**...** do 20 squats in four blocks of five!

While sitting down**...** stretch one leg out, flex your foot, point your foot and circle it five times.

When you reach for your phone**...** instead, go and take a walk around the garden or the house, and get some blood pumping!

When you get out of bed**...** stretch your arms all the way up and round, then stretch your back and each leg. Wake that body up!

When you're in a phone queue**...** do 20 star jumps in two lots of 10.

Can you think of more fun exercises to incorporate into your day?

....

....

....

....

....

ACHIEVE YOUR GOALS!

Learning how to dance, play the guitar, and understand a new language are all brilliant goals, but starting them can be a daunting prospect. The answer to this is easy: think about your main objective and then break it down.

If you want to learn a new language, for example, write down individual action points, like below:

- Sign up to a beginner's class
- Download a language app
- Ask colleagues, friends, or family if anyone speaks that language already
- Practise for ten minutes every day

Or if you want to get fit, break it down to:

- Find an activity that you enjoy, whether it's yoga, rugby, walking, or trampolining.
- Plan in some time each week for your chosen activity.
- Start slow, perhaps with a three-mile walk or a 15-minute yoga session.
- Gradually build up the amount of time or distance you are achieving with your activity, until it hits a comfortable amount.

Create your own plans for achieving your goal in steps, by filling in the following:

My end goal is: ....

These are the steps I'm going to take to achieve my end goal:

....

....

....

My end goal is to: ....

These are the steps I'm going to take to achieve my end goal:

....

....

....

My end goal is to: ....

These are the steps I'm going to take to achieve my end goal:

....

....

....

Planning Your Time

Weekly To-Do List:

Planning your time effectively is very important for making your mind feel strong, tidy, and in control. Your time is so precious, so it's good to make the most of it and get jobs done. It's also crucial to ensure that you're giving yourself enough time to relax and do something purely for enjoyment. The balance is important.

Write down jobs that need to get done this week:

....

....

Write down some nice things to do for relaxation:

....

....

Write down a few activities that show yourself some self-love:

....

....

....

What other commitments or appointments do you have?

....

My Weekly Planner

Now transfer all of those jobs, tasks, and wind-down moments into this weekly planner. Where should they all fit? Feel free to add further points or to take some away, depending on how busy your week gets or how many impromptu jobs happen. Just make sure that you don't sacrifice too many me-time moments!

Monday ....

....

Tuesday ....

....

Wednesday ....

....

Thursday ....

....

Friday ....

....

Saturday ....

....

Sunday ....

....

CREATING CONNECTIONS

Creating and keeping connections with other people is so beneficial for maintaining a strong mind. Having healthy, happy connections with friends and family provide friendship, support, companionship, love, and conversation. This can help people to feel wanted, necessary, and together.

List five ways to create connections with other people:

....

....

....

....

....

....

Do you keep in regular connection with your family and friends?

Yes ☐ No ☐

Is it crucial to nurture connections?

Yes ☐ No ☐

On a scale of 1–10, how connected do you feel to friends and family?

☐ /10

Why do you think connections are important?

....

What more could you do to help maintain connections?

....

Which three people would you like to nurture your connection with?

....

....

....

For each of those people, plan when you're going to nurture your connection with them and how. For example, "I'm going to ring my friend twice a week on Mondays and Thursdays."

....

....

....

....

....

....

....

MEDITATION ON THE DAILY

What do you know about meditation?

....

....

....

Meditation is not just about finding a zen state of mind, or achieving a higher level of being. Instead, it's possible to find meditative moments in everyday tasks. In fact, the most boring of chores can be perfect for allowing our minds relaxation and the ability to be in the present. So, tune into each of your senses, one by one, and turn dull moments into positive, mindful ones.

The list below shows some day-to-day tasks. Each of these could accommodate some meditation, and this would make the experience more enjoyable overall. Can you think of more jobs?

- Vacuuming around the house.
- Taking a bath/shower.
- Going for a walk or a jog.
- Cleaning teeth.
- Cooking some dinner.
- Washing up.

....

....

....

....

....

....

....

....

....

....

....

....

POSITIVE PLAYLIST

If a meditative state is escaping you and the sound of your own stressed-out voice is too loud to tune out, try listening to soothing sounds or songs. Experiment with sounds of rainfall, birdsong, or classical music. Find out what works for you to best quieten your stressed-out thoughts.

Write your own peaceful playlist below and refer back to this page when you need some music inspiration:

HAPPY POSTS

Social media should be a place for positivity, full of upbeat comments, loads of likes, idea-sharing, memorable photos, and creating connections.
Get some ideas together on how to be positive online and write down some pretend posts in the spaces below.

Name five ways to strengthen your mind:

- ....
- ....
- ....
- ....
- ....

Name five ways to strengthen your body:

- ....
- ....
- ....
- ....
- ....

What's the importance of a strong mind and body?

....

On a scale of 1-10, how are you feeling right now? ☐

Write down a favourite affirmation:

....

What was your favourite breathing exercise?

....

Name a mantra that really spoke to you:

....

My Notes

Use this space to jot down any thoughts, feelings, or notes you would like to document. It could be a positive phrase, ideas, feel-good activities, or new pieces of information.

....

....

....

....

....

....